WELLINGTON SQUARE

Afraid of the water

TESSA KRAILING

ILLUSTRATED BY
JON DAVIS

Nelson

'I like to swim,' said Rocky.
'It is my favourite sport.'
'It is not my favourite sport,' said Ben.
'Quick, Ben. We want to get into the water,'
said Rocky.

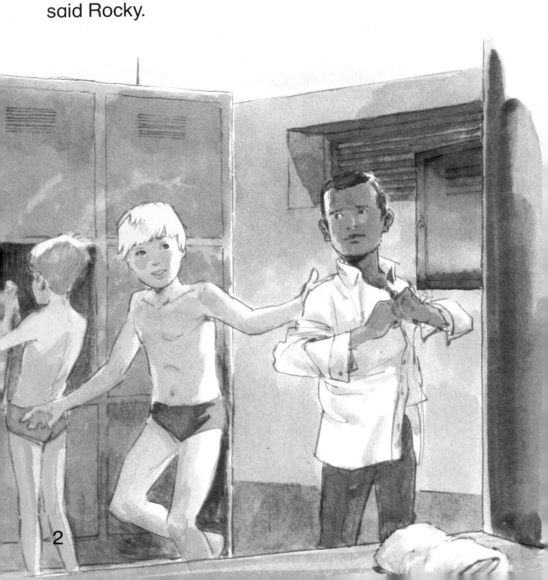

Ben did not like to swim.
He was afraid of the water.
He was afraid he might drown.

'Look at Ben!' shouted Kevin.
'He is always in the shallow end.
He will not go where it is deep.
And I know why! He can't swim!
He can't swim!'

5

'Come on, Ben,' said Mr Belter.
'You must try to swim.
Kick out with your feet.
Push the water away with your hands.'

6

'I know why Ben is always in the shallow end,'
said Kevin.
'He is afraid he will drown.'

Ben was unhappy.
He went home on his own.
If only he could swim!

He was good at sport.
He was good on the trampoline.
He could kick a ball and run.
If only he could swim!

Suddenly there was a noise.
Some boys by the canal were shouting.
What were they doing?

They had put something in the canal.
Suddenly, Ben could see what it was.
It was a kitten on a dustbin lid.

Ben saw a tree.
It lay across the water.
The dustbin lid was coming over to it.
What could he do?

The kitten was afraid.
It was afraid of the water.

Ben crawled onto the tree.
Could he reach the kitten?
He reached out but it was too far away.
He put out his hand as far as he could.

Splash!
He was off the tree and into the canal!
It was deep and he began to splash around.
He had to swim or he would drown!

16

What had Mr Belter told him?
Kick out with his feet.
Push the water away with his hands.
Now he could swim!

Ben reached the kitten.
He grabbed the lid and kicked out with his feet.
He pushed it across to some grass by the canal.

They had made it! They were safe!
'You are safe now,' Ben said to the kitten.

Ben looked for the children.
They must have run off when he was in the water.
'Come with me,' said Ben to the kitten.
'We can go home now.'

'Why are you wet?' said his mother.
'You look half drowned.'
'I can swim,' said Ben.
'I had to swim to save a kitten from the canal.'

His mother was very cross.
'That was a very silly thing to do.
You might have drowned!' she said.

The next day Ben jumped in the water at
the deep end.
Kevin looked surprised.
'You can swim!' he shouted.

23

Yes, Ben could swim.
He was not afraid of the water.
'That's good,' said Mr Belter.
'You must know how to swim.'
'Now it is my favourite sport,' said Ben.